CHART HITS NOW!

JITAR

GW00375280

HOW WE DO (PARTY)

...PLUS 11 MORE TOP HITS

In order to
by the las

WISE PUBLICATIONS

London / New York /

Hong Kong / Tokyo

Published by
Wise Publications
14-15 Berners Street, London W1T 3LJ, UK.

Exclusive Distributors:

Music Sales Limited
Distribution Centre, Newmarket Road,
Bury St Edmunds, Suffolk IP33 3YB, UK.

Music Sales Pty Limited
20 Resolution Drive, Caringbah,
NSW 2229, Australia.

Order No. AM1005884
ISBN: 978-1-78038-836-6
This book © Copyright 2012 Wise Publications,
a division of Music Sales Limited.

Edited by Jenni Norey.
Cover design by Tim Field.

Printed in the EU.

Black Heart

Words & Music by Shaznay Lewis, Iyiola Babalola,
Darren Lewis & Jo Perry

1. I don't like it when you break me, hon-ey.___ Why'd you have to do that?___
2. No walls to build a-round me, hon-ey.___ 'Cause you blew my house down.___

Tell me, when you make these tears keep fall-in',
Sticks and stones won't put it back up for me,

do you feel like a man?___ Fig - ure, fig - ure, there's no
and that's where we're at now.___ Sick - er, sick - er, I ain't

work - ing you out___ what - so - ev - er.___
feel - ing your mouth___ what - so - ev - er.___

On - ly one way I could sum you up___ al - to - geth - er.___
A name, it hurts me more the way from a - round, but what - ev - er.___

Good Time

Words & Music by Adam Young, Brian Dong Ho Lee
& Matthew Thiessen

What's up with this Prince song in-side my head? Hands up if you're

down to get down_ to-night.__ 'Cause it's al-ways a good_ time.__

2. Slept in all my clothes like I did-n't care. Hopped in-to a
3. Freaked out, dropped my phone in the pool a-gain. Checked out from my

cab, take me an-y-where. I'm in if you're down to get down_ to-night.__
room, hit the A. T. M. Let's hang out if you're down to get down_ to-night.__

Whoa,____ oh, oh, oh, oh.   We don't e-ven have to try,   it's al-ways a good   time.__

1.

(Good time,_ good time.)_   It's al-ways a good   time.____   Whoa,____ oh, oh.

2.

Whoa,____ oh, oh, oh, oh.   Whoa,____ oh.   It's al-ways a good   time_

Whoa,____ oh, oh, oh, oh.   We don't e-ven have to try,   it's al-ways a good   time.__

14

Hall Of Fame

Words & Music by Mark Sheehan, Daniel O'Donoghue,
Will.i.am & James Barry

1. Yeah, you could be the

greatest. You can be the best. You can be the King Kong bang-ing on your chest. You could beat the
(2.) dis-tance. You can run the mile. You can walk straight through hell with a smile. You could be the

world. You could beat the war. You could talk to God, go bang-ing on his door. You can throw your
he-ro. You could get the gold. Break-ing all the re-cords they thought nev-er could be broke. Do it for your

hands up. You can beat the clock. You can move a moun-tain. You can break rocks. You could be a
peo-ple. Do it for your pride. Nev-er gon-na know if you nev-er e-ven try. Do it for your

How We Do (Party)

Words & Music by Hal David, Willie Hutch, Bob West, Jermaine Jackson,
Bonnie McKee, Christopher Wallace, Andrew Harr, Alexander Delicata,
Berry Gordy Jr., Osten Harvey, Kelly Sheehan, Andre Davidson & Sean Davidson

23

Little Talks

Words & Music by Ragnar Thorhallsson & Nanna Bryndis Hilmarsdottir

28

Read All About It, Part III

Words & Music by Shahid Khan & Emeli Sandé

Princess Of China

**Words & Music by Chris Martin, Guy Berryman,
Jon Buckland, Will Champion & Brian Eno**

Once up-on a time we fell a-part. You're hold-ing in your hands the two____ halves of my heart.

Oh.____

Oh.____

44

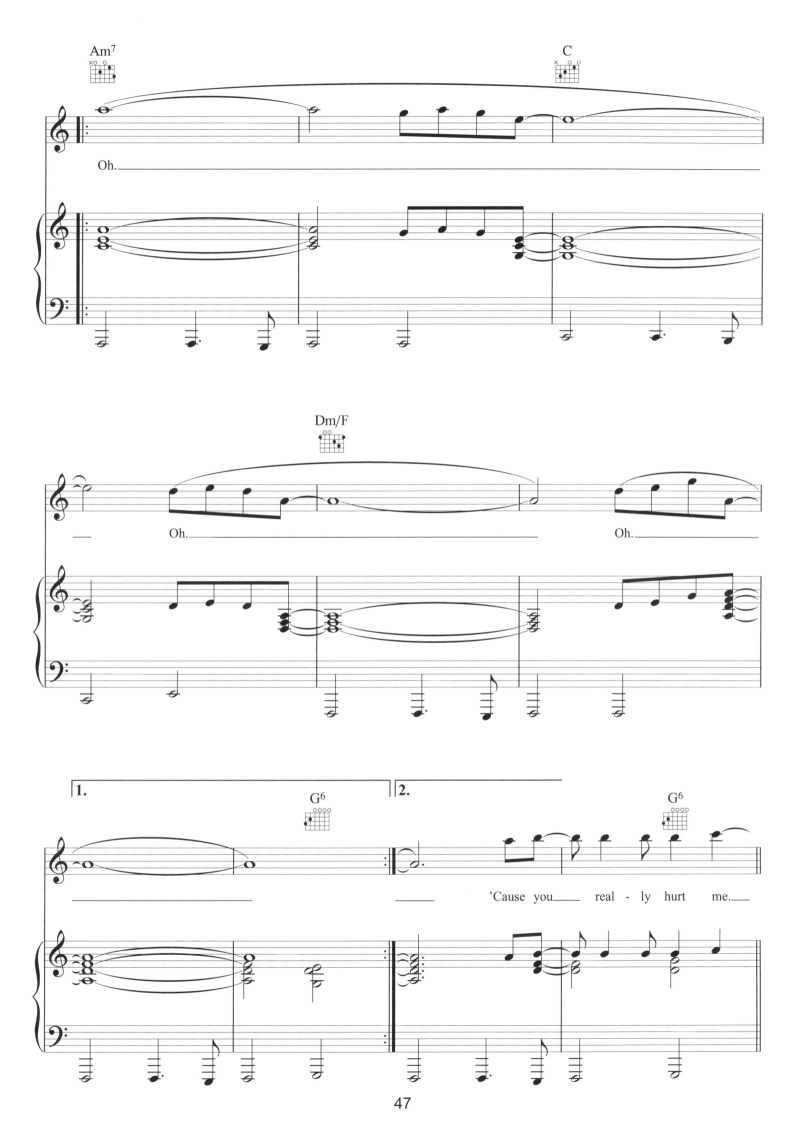

Spectrum

Words & Music by Paul Epworth & Florence Welch

Skinny Love

Words & Music by Justin Vernon

morn-ing I'll__ be with__ you, but it will be a dif-f'rent kind__ 'Cause I'll be
all your love__ is wast-ed, then who the hell__ was I?__ 'Cause now I'm

hold-ing all__ the tick-ets__ and you'll be own-ing all__ the fines.__
break-ing at__ the brit-ches__ and at the ends of all__ your lines.__

To Coda ⊕

3. Come on skin-ny love,__ what hap-pened here?__

Suc-kle on__ the hope__ in lite__ bras-siere.__

Come on skin-ny love._____

My____ my my,____ my my my,____ my my my____ my my.____

My____ my my,____ my my my,____ my my my____ my my.____

Summertime In The City

Words & Music by Roy Stride

1.Sum-mer-time in the cit-y, all the girls dress hot, make the boys go sil-ly. There they go,
-mer 2.Lunch time in the cit-y and we're get-ting in the mood and we're get-ting there quick - ly,   tip-sy.

walk-ing'round the streets down-town on a wan-der. Fake de-sign-er shades,   love in the sum - mer.
Girls watch the boys, boys watch the girls and no one wants to be by them-selves in the world. And it's

We Are Never Ever Getting Back Together

Words & Music by Max Martin, Taylor Swift & Shellback

69

This Is Love

Words & Music by Dallas Austin, William Adams
& Kenneth Oliver

123456789